Author and a Plymouth Rock Hen

My Orpingtons in their Run

The BIG BOOK of GARDEN HENS

Published in 2001
by Kitchen Garden Books
The Kitchen Garden
Church Lane
Troston
Bury St Edmunds
Suffolk IP31 1EX
01359 268 322
francine@jfraymond.demon.co.uk

ISBN 0-9532857-3-1

With many thanks to Charlie and Gabrielle for their wonderful portraits of the birds, to Penny for her recipes and the lunches when we tested them, to Jenny at J L Design for her computer expertise, to Annabel Whittet for her help with the printers, to Miss Jo Kendall for her reader's overview and to all at the Henhouse* for their help with the hens.

The BIG BOOK of GARDEN HENS

FRANCINE RAYMOND

Recipes
PENELOPE HANDS

Photos
CHARLIE COLMER

Illustrations
GABRIELLE STODDART

A Kitchen Garden Book

This book is laid out in chapters. Each one concentrates on a particular aspect of henkeeping. Each section also highlights two breeds and gives month by month advice to encourage you and your flock through the year. On the last page of each chapter Penny Hands offers a seasonal recipe to make use of the glut of eggs I'm sure your hens will provide.

CONTENTS

Introduction

Throughout the book * refers to information in the Directory

INTRODUCTION

I've been keeping hens for about ten years. Not a lifetime I know, and certainly not long enough to justify the *sobriquet* Chicken Woman or be considered an expert. But unlike most writers of books on poultry, I'm not a professional breeder with a huge flock nor do I show them. I just keep a few hens in my garden, like you do - for fun, for their eggs and their charm. Their presence cheers me and their manure enriches the soil. Without them, I'd find my life the poorer - not to mention my cooking and compost.

What I find particularly satisfying is the link between kitchen, garden and hens. Plants and birds produce to their full potential: the flock feasts on kitchen and garden waste, and flowers and vegetables thrive on chicken manure. In return your hens' delicious fresh eggs - the only really fresh eggs around - will feed you and your family a wide range of dishes; just take a look at Penny Hands' mouth-watering selection of recipes.

If you're a beginner wanting to keep hens, you may like to refer to our book Keeping a Few Hens in your Garden.* It gives all the salient instructions without overloading you with information which, though interesting is not essential at this point. You could then progress to this book.

I find most henkeepers fall into two categories. Those like me, who have a few fowl and are obsessed by their personalities and the flock dynamic. The others, charmed by every breed, buy them all and leave them to get on with life, ending up with far too many birds, broods and crossbreeds. This strategy is completely free range with little human interference, and even fewer eggs for the kitchen. It is glorious fun for a while but eventually you

8

end up with mostly cockerels plus a few beleaguered hens who are abused and die off, leaving a posse of badly behaved louts.

Let the amount of space you can spare (not your egg needs or passing fancies for different breeds) determine how many birds you keep. Most fowl problems are caused by stress and overcrowding. At the risk of sounding like a chicken run dictator, firm management is needed. If you keep hens without a cock, life is easy. You can confine them demurely like convent girls, and rest safe in the knowledge there'll be no hatchings, no over-amorous advances or noisy alarm calls. The pecking order persists - the stability of the flock depends on it - and the top hen will be as demanding as a mother superior.

My flock boasts a Buff Orpington cockerel with six or seven wives of different ages. Every year I hatch a couple of chicks and an old lady drops off the other end of the perch. I get new bloodlines by buying in hatching eggs and can afford to be sentimental because I don't have to select birds like showmen or breeders. My interest isn't just in pure breeds, except to ensure their survival, I'm just as fond of my crosses - they make far better mums than my big Orpington ladies.

There are as many ways of looking after poultry as there are fashions in childrearing. Pick a system that suits you and enjoy yourself, ignore the avian mother-in-laws tut tutting away. I spend hours with my hens working in the garden and most summer evenings I take a glass of wine and sit in the hammock, slung between two old apple trees in the chicken run and just watch them. Poultrymaid's perks.

Appenzeller Hen

Linda's White Silkie Hen

STARTING POINTS

Hens have been our backyard partners since time began. We've lived side by side and evolved together. They have provided us with eggs, meat, and feathers. I'm not sure we've been so good to them.

DNA testing has proved that today's chickens are descended from several types of small pheasant-like Jungle fowl originating in Java, Ceylon and Burma. Domestication has made them bigger and encouraged them to lay regularly. There is evidence that the early Egyptians hatched eggs in giant incubators, and at the pinnacle of the Roman Empire cocks were deified and augured outcomes of battle. They were used as timepieces and carried as mascots into the thick of the fight.

Chickens arrived in these islands via the Romans and later traders. Regional variations: the Dorking, Marsh Daisy, Scots Dumpy and Scots Grey, Derbyshire Redcap, Sussex, Old English Game and Pheasant Fowl were developed for meat, eggs or cockfighting. The Asiatic breeds arrived in the mid 19th century as a present to Queen Victoria of a pair of Cochins and opened up a range of opportunities to British breeders like William Cook. Breeding hens became all the rage - poultrymania spread throughout this country and America. The ban on cockfighting spawned the sport of exhibiting - still a rather macho preserve.

The wartime Dig for Victory campaign turned every back garden into a chicken run with half a dozen hens, fed with foul steaming saucepans of mash, and cheered on by local poultry advisers. Government involvement in postwar food policy encouraged farmers to bring flocks undercover to protect them from predators, creating ideal opportunities for disease. Pure breeds were hybridized to create birds to feed and lay cheaply for the burgeoning population; broodiness was eradicated and hybrids were easy to sex. Stressful living conditions encouraged bad habits, and farmers retaliated with even more devious schemes. The birds got sicker and became impervious to the antibiotics on which they were routinely fed.

All this is evident today in the appearance and taste of the eggs and chicken fed to the public. The current backlash to battery farming has not just stemmed from our abhorrence of poultry living conditions, but our refusal to eat such second-rate fare. Public opinion and EEC legislation has encouraged farmers to set up freerange units, but I still believe the only way to get a really fresh egg is to keep your own hens.

By keeping pure breeds you'll not only help ensure the future of these beautiful birds but retain their valuable habits and characteristics, lost in their relations crammed in battery cages. It is from this stock that successful freerange flocks will be bred.

This is my blueprint for a small garden flock:

Phase I - Buy two pure breed hens and a crossbreed (preferably from a good line of broodies).

Phase II - Buy two more pure breed hens, or 6 hatching eggs to put under your broody (probably 50% success rate).

Phase III - Likely at least one of the eggs will hatch out to be a cockerel.

Phase IV - From then on try and hatch a couple of hens per year. By this time the oldest hens will be out of lay, can retire and be replaced with chicks.

This system ensures a constant supply of eggs, because the youngest hen will lay throughout her first year and the others are all at different stages of lay. As a novice henkeeper you will have been broken in gently. You can leave out the cock altogether and buy in fertile hatching eggs, but the risk of hatching cockerels is always there. Alternatively you could buy in a couple of hens annually, but the problems of introducing newcomers and possible new diseases persist. It is for you to decide.

If I've convinced you to keep hens for the first time, you should now contact the Environmental Health Officer at your Town Hall to check if there are any contra-indications to your having poultry, especially if you live in a built-up area. Discuss your plans with your neighbours to see if they'll help while you're on holiday and are prepared to put up with the noise (just the odd contented cluck if you avoid cocks).

JANUARY
Timely Advice

- Resolve to clean out your henhouse more frequently.
- Hens are well insulated and don't mind the cold, but hate wind and wet.
- Order some bales of straw and build a shelter in the run.
- Hens will sometimes stay in their house all day, especially if it snows.
- Make sure the house is airy but that any ventilation is above head height.
- A hessian flap nailed inside the pophole will stop daytime draughts.
- Board the fence or place a straw bale opposite their pophole.
- Ensure the house is insulated with newspaper and clean, dry straw.
- If it's icy, move water containers to a sheltered spot and re-fill regularly. A plastic flowerpot saucer makes a good temporary drinker and the frozen water can be knocked out easily.

COCHIN
(see also p 21)
China
13lb - 5.90kg (cock's weight)

Big and round and reliable with children, the Cochin, originally called the Shanghai, caused a furore in 1845, when a pair was presented to Queen Victoria as a wedding present. Exaggerations about their fabled size spread throughout the land. Bred by Chinese for bulk meat, smallish eggs, and for feathers, the Buffs look like huge ginger duvets. Well-wattled and crested they are calm and massive, but have a tendency to fat and heart problems. The Cochin is not unlike an Orpington with feathered legs. Both need to be given space on the lawn to keep fit. There is a famous flock at Chatsworth. Even, solid colours: buff, white, black, blue, cuckoo and also partridge.

ORPINGTON
(see p 102)
Great Britain
12lb - 5.50kg

William Cook bred the Black Orpington in 1886, and then established the Buffs, followed by white and blue. The Blacks make good pets with lovely beetlewing feathers, but utility has been diluted at the expense of fluff. The Buffs, though of stout and matronly mien, are surprisingly energetic. Apart from their obvious charms, it's ultimately their friendliness I love - it's nice to be liked - even by a chicken. Laying small tinted eggs, they were also bred for the table. I've said it before, but eating your Buff Orpington would be like dining on the family labrador. Beloved of their patron, the Queen Mother, her flock is looked after by Mr Burdett, author of the seminal work on the breed.* Sadly their health is being sacrificed for size.

SEVILLE ORANGE OR LEMON CURD

If you're lucky, your hens will start laying while Seville oranges are still in season, but you can of course make lemon curd at any time. Seville orange curd is the perfect marriage of buttery richness and sharp citrus, and makes a wonderful tart filling if you double the quantities.

2 large whole eggs plus 2 yolks
4oz/125g unsalted butter, cubed
4oz/125g caster sugar
Grated rind and juice of 2 large lemons or 2 Seville oranges

Beat the eggs and egg yolks together in a jug. Put the cubed butter, sugar and grated lemon or orange rind and juice into a basin. (Use a zester to grate your fruit - it's much easier than a traditional grater). Pour the eggs in through a sieve. Put the basin over a saucepan of simmering water and cook, stirring regularly, until the curd is really thick - about 20 minutes. While it is cooking, wash a large jam jar in hot water and dry it in a low oven. Boil the lid for a few minutes to sterilize it. Spoon the curd into the warm jar, seal and leave to cool. Store in the fridge, but eat within two weeks before it loses its fresh taste.

A Partridge Cochin Cock

A Welsummer Hen

CHICKEN RUNS

Although my flock has access to my ²/₃ acre garden most of the time, I have a run in a small orchard where the henhouses and feed bins are kept, and birds can be isolated if necessary. The chicken wire fence is about head height and now completely hidden by a yew hedge and climbing plants. The wire is pegged at its base with wire skewers or tent pegs, and the run offers plenty of shelter from wind and rain, and shade from the sun. We have a shed (my sons' recording studio) with a covered verandah where the hens vibrate gloomily defying the bad weather. And the musicians often leave with reminders of my flock on their trainers.

Give your hens as much space as you can, especially if you want them to spend a lot of time there. In a full-time run it is best to fence and divide the space in two, with the henhouse in the middle and popholes to both sides, so you can rotate your birds and rest the other half of the run. Old chicken runs were panelled with corrugated iron up to knee height offering extra shelter. You could use close-boarded fencing or strategically positioned straw bales Angle the entrance to your henhouse away from the prevailing wind.

The chicken run in Winter is not a lovesome place, especially if you garden on heavy soil. It will get very muddy. Use a wooden pallet as a plinth for feed bins and drinkers. Recently I bought some rigid galvanized wire panels to use as gates, hurdles or joined together as partitions, free standing cages or duck boards. Scaffolding boards will protect the grass en route to your chicken run, as would decking panels and roll up paths or permanent paving slabs. Take care not to slip on your way. Cover the floor of the run with dry leaves or straw. A small graveled area by the pophole will stop chickens taking mud inside the house. Remember your flock will always make their own way to roost at night, so if you can let them out into the garden, even for a short time, perhaps as you get back from work, they will soon get used to the routine and the run will get a rest.

Shade is as important as shelter. Large shrubs and trees (with flints or big pebbles placed to protect their roots) are ideal, but you could make shade during heatwaves with bamboo or willow panels. Short grass is good for hens, so by rotating their quarters you can make sure it's always available. I dig up part of the run if my hens are *in situ*, it keeps them busy and the area is ready to re-seed when they move on.

Make your chicken run as safe and attractive as you can, it doesn't have to look like Cold Comfort Farm. Paint the timber posts and gates to match your colour scheme and grow climbers and roses up the wire or trellis - they will appreciate the extra manure. Keep an old folding garden seat inside, so you can relax there too.

If you live in a foxy area, security is going to be a priority. A run with a wire roof and the bottom 6″ of the fence buried underground is essential. Use chicken wire with small gauge holes so hens can't stick their heads through. Stronger weld mesh fencing is a good idea but rather expensive. The henhouse we've designed has an integral weldmesh run and you can leave food and water in there for early breakfasts. Site a house like this inside a high security run and you may be lucky. Cut away any overhanging branches from surrounding trees.

There are sonic devices that are pitched to deter dogs and cats, and electric fences, but a determined fox will put up with any discomfort for a good meal. Site your run as near to your house as possible. Foxes scavenge for food at dawn, so if you're an early riser too, keep an ear open. If you live in a country area with a shoot, you'll find the keepers are keen to protect their pheasant poults and so foxes will be rarer than in a hunting county. Urban and suburban foxes are the cheekiest of the lot, because they've become used to human company. Sometimes it just isn't worth the heartbreak and expense, so shelve your henkeeping plans for another time or place.

Please don't use those little arks with minute runs for anything other than two tiny bantams or a broody and chicks. Even though you can push them round the garden to pastures new every day, they are far too confined a space for anything other than the smallest of hens - especially with a cock, except as a good safe bedroom inside a bigger run.

Hens need constant access to fresh drinking water. I have an Eltex* galvanized drinker that re-fills itself from a central container and is kept in the run. It needs regular cleaning and scouring. I leave large terracotta flowerpot saucers strategically placed around the garden, rainwater seems to be preferred - but these need changing or the water turns to soup but I often see my hens drinking from the fetid duckpond by choice. Grain can be scattered around the run, but not in the evening when anything that isn't eaten straight away should be fed in a removable container. There is a wide range of poultry feeders,* some designed to deter other diners. Select one to suit the size of your flock and the frequency you feed them.

FEBRUARY
Timely Advice

○ When you are sorting out compost heaps, remember that chicken manure makes an excellent activator between the layers.

○ Let your flock into fruit cages to eat pests and manure the fruit bushes.

○ Now is a good time to repair henhouses and runs.

○ Have a good clean-out with disinfectant and re-paint with Cuprinol.*

○ If you find your henhouse has passed its sell-by date, order a new one.

○ February 14th - traditionally the time when hens start to lay after the winter break. Make sure they have extra protein and offer poultry spice.

○ Protect any susceptible new bulb growth with cloches.

○ Shrove Tuesday - Pancake Day, add an extra egg to your batter.

○ Look out for frostbite on cocks' combs - Vaseline will protect them.

BRAHMA
(see p 31)
Asia
12lbs - 5.50kg

These tall, aristocratic gentle giants of the henworld used to be known as rich men's pets because they're not hugely productive and eat a lot. Carla Carlisle who runs a flock in her orchard loves them for their looks and their friendliness. They're easy to handle (she was interviewed recently on television with a Brahma hen sitting quietly on her lap). Dressed by Armani, the Light, Dark, Gold have beautifully pencilled plumage, heavily feathered legs, a small peacomb and heavy eyebrows. There are also pure white Brahmas and Buff Columbians with black cuff and tail feathers. The females are shorter legged and easy to differentiate when chicks.

DORKING
(see p 52)
Great Britain
12lbs - 5.50 kg

A noble breed, brought over by the Romans, who prized them for their fine white meat. Dorkings are well wattled, have five toes, short legs and look rather horizontal. Active, wide ranging and needing plenty of space, Judith Phillips at Kentwell, a Tudor Hall in Long Melford keeps them for their historical significance. She loves her flock but finds them a bit slow-witted. The Dorking is long lived, but slow to mature. Even the hen has lovely coloured plumage. Apparently not good for damp gardens, one wonders how it has survived for so long in this country. There are also Silver and Dark Dorkings that need support, as does the breed as a whole.

29

SOUFFLE IN A SOUP BOWL
The recipes in this book are for 4 people.

These green and gold soufflés look pretty baked in four old-fashioned shallow soup plates, but check that all four plates will fit in your oven before you start.

¹/₂oz/5g butter
4 tablespoons grated Parmesan cheese
4 large eggs separated
4oz/125g fresh soft goat's cheese
4oz/125g cooked chopped spinach
2 tablespoons double cream or crème fraîche
1 tablespoon chopped chervil or tarragon
Salt and pepper

Preheat your oven 400F/200C.
Butter four soup plates and sprinkle with 1 tablespoon of Parmesan. Whisk the egg yolks until smooth, whisk in the goat's cheese, and stir in the cream. Add the spinach, chopped herbs and half the remaining Parmesan. Season quite strongly with salt and black pepper.

In a separate bowl, whisk the egg whites till stiff but not dry. Fold the whites into the cheese base, spoon into the plates and sprinkle with the rest of the Parmesan. Bake in the oven for 8 - 10 minutes. They should look quite moist, as they go on cooking in the plates for a while. Serve immediately, but be careful - the soufflés and plates will be very hot.

This recipe scales down easily for a quick lunch for one.

Carla Carlisle's Light Brahmas at Wyken

31

Leslie Geddes-Brown's Marans Cock and Hen

HENHOUSES

Choose a pretty henhouse that looks good in your garden. Indulge in a little fantasy - a Gothic chapel, a Georgian mansion, or a Post Modern *palais-de-poulets* - mine look like Southwold bathing huts. Even just painting a basic house (available from the companies* listed at the end of this book) with Sadolin or Cuprinol* shades to fit in with your garden's overall colour scheme can be a huge improvement. You could customize an existing shed or kennel provided it has good apex ventilation, and my husband has drawn plans of our latest design for you to interpret.

We suggest Onduline* for roofs because it doesn't harbour parasites, prevents condensation, is light and comes in a good range of colours. Heavy falls of snow should be scraped off though, because I've noticed it leaks a bit as the snow melts. If you keep large hens, some won't perch, don't worry, they'll be happy on the floor. For others place perches no higher than 8″ (20cm) off the ground and bevel the top edge for comfortable roosting. Make sure you have an efficient drop door with a catch, and a lock if you are worried about unwelcome visitors.

Build your house on legs or on a plinth with a ramp for your hens. It will be easier on your back as you clean up. The space underneath will provide shelter plus an excellent dustbath for your hens; and being accessible to cats, won't be the sort of spot rats like to lurk. Dustbathing in dry soil removes parasites. You could add a little powdered charcoal or ashes. Hens love a good dustbath, they seem to go into a trance. They also sunbathe, often with one leg and wing outstretched.

I have several small houses so my birds have a choice of residence. Newcomers have a place to call their own, old ladies can be by themselves, squabbles don't continue to bedtime and layers can choose a quiet spot. You should put a movable 1ft/30cm square nestbox inside your house, away from light for all to lay in. Fill it with straw and add a 3"/7cm lip to stop the bedding falling out. Hens like to lay in secret places with even the access away from public gaze - I have a separate nest house with a *trompe l'oeil* door plus occupant painted on the front, while the real hen hops in the real door at the back. Extra small houses can turn into hospitals or nurseries.

You have a choice of bedding materials. If you want to use straw, I recommend dust-free chopped straw,* better for you and your flock, or wood shavings, but they take ages to rot down on the compost heap. Never use hay, it can harbour moulds which are bad for hens. It is the build-up of ammonia from droppings that harms birds' lungs, so regular mucking out and adequate ventilation - especially in hot weather is essential, not just for fastidiousness' sake but to keep your flock in good health. Hens do two thirds of their total droppings at night apparently and each one can produce a staggering hundredweight of droppings in a year.

I clean out my henhouses once a week. Wearing attractive rubber gloves I sweep out the debris with a small hand brush, using a decorator's scraper for those stubborn bits. I then cover the floor of the house with lots of sheets of newspaper. Next time I clean, these can easily be scooped out, and the droppings, (hopefully - 'firm and capped with white - indicating the good health of the occupants') are shaken onto the compost heap and the paper is shredded. As carbon-rich waste the newspaper will layer nicely between additions of nitrogen-rich manure and kitchen and garden waste. Big wodges of newsprint take too long to rot down, (good soaked to fill the bottom of runner bean trenches though) but they can be wetted in a bucket to form a foul *papier mâché* and then put on the heap. When collecting eggs, I turn over a few pages - instant clean bedding. It amuses me to see my hens settling down for the night on the pink financial pages or more extreme fashion features.

Have a real Spring clean every three months and disinfect with Jeyes Fluid. Look up into the roof, you'll see a cathedral of cobwebs, festooned with dust. Blitz them with a car hoover. Look out for red mites. They are fat and slow and 1mm long. Dust the house with mite repellent.* The other main parasite that lives on the hen herself is the yellow-coloured louse (2mm). Dust affected birds round the neck and vent with louse powder.* After the clean-up, leave plenty of time to air the house before bedtime.

If you decide on a ready-made henhouse, be sceptical about the number of occupants the makers boast it will hold. I don't like arks unless they are more than 4′ high, because the lack of headroom can damage crests. Space needed per bird for perch, nestbox or pophole: 15″sq/35sq cm per huge hen; 1sq ft/30sq cm per large hen or 9″sq/25sq cm per bantam. Make it easy for yourself to be a conscientious poultrymaid. I would love a henhouse that I could get into too. It could be a garden shed - I'm not asking much - so I could spend more time with my hens in the evening when we're all relaxed. I have a lovely old book about keeping bantams and the author suggests, 'a hook inside the door so a gentleman could hang up his coat and feel at home'. Bliss.

OUR DESIGN FOR A HENHOUSE

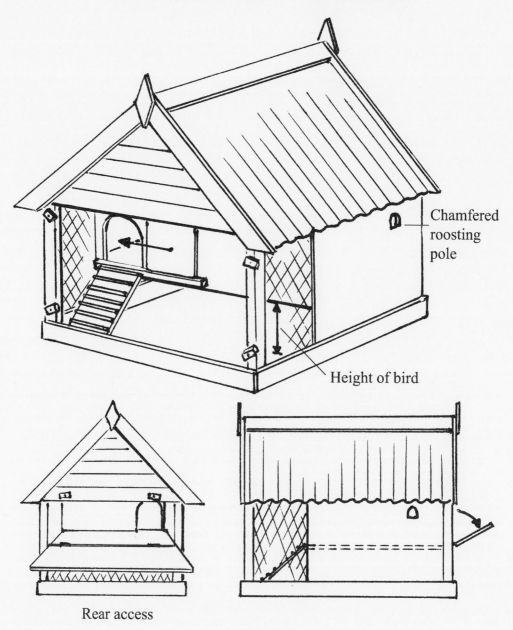

Chamfered
roosting
pole

Height of bird

Rear access

MARCH
Timely Advice

- Time to order fertile eggs from your breeder, or swop with a friend.
- Also order any new birds, so they can be hatched and ready for you at point-of-lay (about 20-24 weeks). You can take them as soon as they can be sexed, but pullets need separate accommodation.
- If new growth in your garden is under threat, keep your hens in the run.
- Dig up part of the run and re-seed when they have moved on.
- To stop your hens escaping from their run, get help and trim the first three flight feathers on one wing, see p115.
- Collect eggs regularly or your hens will go broody.
- Plant vegetable seeds in pots under cover so they have a head start.

SUSSEX
(see p 41)
Great Britain
10lbs - 4.10kg

Broad breasted and plump, this is one of the oldest utility dual-purpose breeds to be developed in this country. The brown Speckled was the first variety. The more famous Light Sussex with its graphically pencilled matching black cuff and tail feathers is a later development. Also comes in plain white, buff, silver, brown and red. They lay lots of tinted eggs for at least five years, are easy to hatch and make good mums. They were used with RIR to produce first sex linkage crosses, and with Indian Game to make the first broilers. Joanna Mayer* breeds Sussex near here and tells me they are hardy and disease-resistant, love free-ranging - distance no object. Both hens and cockerels are docile and she 'has never known a nasty one'.

ROCK
(see p 1)
United States
9lb - 3.40kg

Prolific layers of tinted eggs, solid, plump and strong, the barred Rocks look like Victorian gentlemen bathers in stripy grey and cream costumes. They have lovely markings and are also available in plain white, buff, black and the rare Columbian. The barred lay best. Jacqui Collier's flock of Buff Rocks is famously serenaded by Radio 3 to encourage them to lay. She chose Buff Rocks because her mother recommended them as good natured dual purpose birds, and her own experience is of gentlemen cockerels - faithful and protective, and productive hens. Their buff plumage is quieter than the ginger/buff of the Orpington. Nice, cosy birds, but standard Buff Rocks are now quite difficult to find in this country.

FRITTATA OF SWISS CHARD AND PARSLEY

A *frittata* is an Italian omelette - served flat not rolled, and usually eaten at room temperature - it makes good picnic food served with Italian bread.

6-8 eggs
4 tablespoons flat-leaved parsley
4 large blanched, chopped chard leaves without ribs
1 tablespoon olive oil
Salt and pepper

Preheat the oven to 400F/200C.

Beat the eggs together vigorously in a bowl and stir in the parsley and chard. Season lightly with salt and pepper. Heat the oil in a large oven-proof frying pan and pour in the egg mixture. Cook over a low heat for about ten minutes until the eggs are beginning to set, then transfer to the oven to brown and set the top. Don't overcook or it will be dry and stodgy. Remove from the oven and loosen the edges. Put an upturned plate on top and turn over. Serve at room temperature, cut in wedges. A blob of sour cream or Greek yogurt goes well with this dish, plus lots of crusty bread.

Using this method, you can make a *frittata* with any combination of seasonal vegetables and herbs. I particularly like baby peas and mint, or leek and spinach or broccoli and garlic. Blanch or cook the vegetables first till they are just *al dente* and then follow this recipe.

Light Sussex Hens

41

Buff Columbian Brahma Cock and Exchequer Leghorn Hen

BREEDS

There are over a hundred breeds of chicken for you to choose from. The selection in this book includes birds for beginners, some for fun, for eggs, good looks, and some breeds that need help. Remember that hens bred for their beauty have probably lost their utility characteristics. You can keep a flock of different sized breeds and crossbreeds. Size isn't always paramount in the pecking order - my top hens have always been bantam crosses.

Farmyard crossbreeds are a random mixture of two or more types, like mongrels. The resulting hens are often good layers with natural vigour and beautiful plumage. Long-lived, hardy and disease resistant, they make good mums and broodies, especially Silkie and bantam crosses, though the latter are sometimes bad tempered. We had one called the Nasty Hen who mothered all my Orpingtons - luckily they did not inherit her dislike of people or her baleful eye.

Hybrids on the other hand are 'designed' by scientists, either for egg production or as meat, usually for battery life, though more recently for free range. In both cases the genes are selected for maximum production at the earliest age, so these birds are short-lived, can't cope with weather or even carry their own weight. I correspond regularly with the English owner, in France of Chickpea aka *Pois Chiche*, who led a charmed life, escaping from a lorry as a day old chick. Purpose-built accommodation, loving care, home cooking and even charming companions Madeleine and Albertine could not prolong his lucky but nonetheless short life.

Most hybids are combinations of Rhode Island Reds, Light Sussex and Rocks. Others are crossed to produce really good brown eggs, like those from Scotland Place Farm* near here. Mr Munson* keeps Leghorn crosses laying white eggs for Delia Smith amongst others, and Philip Lee-Woolf at Clarence Court Farm* has a flock of Legbars (Leghorn, Rocks, Araucana and others) that lay blue/green eggs ranging from azure to the palest blue.

Chickens come in two sizes, standard and bantam. Some say the latter originate from the town of Bantam in East Indies where the natives sold their tiny birds to English traders in the 17th century. A quarter of the size of the standard version of their breed, they take up less space, eat less, but lay smaller and less frequent eggs. They are easy to tame, do less damage in the garden, but on the other hand are often noisier, flighty and the cocks can be aggressive. I prefer the big ones. There are also some naturally small breeds like the Pekins, Sebrights, Silkies, and the Dutch, Belgian and Japanese bantams. These don't have larger counterparts, but possess many of the reputed advantages of bantams. A couple of these pretty little birds make ideal inhabitants for a small garden but are not prolific layers.

I recommend the breeds in this book from my own and friends' experience. Prices vary hugely. It obviously makes sense as a beginner to choose birds that are less expensive, and if you have a tiny garden to think about bantams or small breeds. Hens come spangled, speckled, barred, laced, bearded, muffed, crested and pom-pommed. Whichever you choose, go and see them before you buy, checking all are healthy and have been well cared for.

My choices are displayed in colour throughout this book and are listed in order of weight and drawn to scale with their vital statistics, two per chapter. (The cocks' maximum weights to Poultry Club standards, are included to give an indication of their size. Hens usually weigh from 4lb(1.80kg) to 4oz (100g) less depending on size, thus an Orpington hen weighs 4lbs less but a Pekin hen is a mere 4 oz lighter than her mate).

On the following page you will see a list of the majority of breeds commonly available in this country. On pages 108 and 109 all our chosen breeds are illustrated together in a double spread so you can judge who's who and check their relative sizes.

LIST OF BREEDS COMMONLY AVAILABLE
(Those featured in this book are italicized).

Ancona	Hamburgh	*Orpington Buff*
Andalusian	Houdan	Orpington Black
Appenzeller	Indian Game	*Pekin*
Araucana	Ixworth	*Plymouth Rock*
Asil	Japanese	Poland
Australorp	Jersey Giant	*Rhode Island Red*
Barnevelder	Kraienkopf	Rosecomb
Barbu D'Anvers	Lakenvelder	Scots Dumpy
Barbu D'Uccles	La Flèche	Scots Grey
Belgian Watermael	*Leghorn*	*Sebright*
Brahma	Malay	Sicilian Buttercup
Campine	*Marans*	*Silkie*
Cochin	Marsh Daisy	Spanish
Crèvecoeur	Minorca	Sultan
Croad Langshan	Modern Game	Sumatra
Derbyshire Redcap	Nankin	*Sussex*
Dorking	Norfolk Grey	Tuzo
Faverolles	North Holland Blue	Vorwerk
Fayoumi	Old English Game	*Welsummer*
Friesian	Old English Pheasant	*Wyandotte*
Frizzle	Orloff	Yokohama

APRIL
Timely Advice

- If you want to hatch eggs, always date them with a soft pencil.
- They will stay viable for two to three weeks.
- Make a note of when your broody starts to sit and what eggs she has.
- Calculate hatching day. 21 days from the time the broody sits - not from the time the eggs were laid.
- Check your cockerel's spurs, blunt with a hacksaw and file smooth p 56.
- Isolate him if he is over-ardent.
- Cover new grass sowings with clear plastic until germinated, then protect with black nylon netting.
- Decorate Easter eggs. For a longer lasting egg - hard boil for two hours.
- Make delicious homemade marzipan with your eggs for Simnel cake.

RHODE ISLAND RED

(see p 51)

United States

9lbs - 3.85kg

Possibly the best known breed in the world was developed at the turn of the century. Having a special place in most people's memory, the Rhody is the traditional-looking brown hen that lays lots of brown eggs. A good forager and hardy, RIR are the basis with Sussex of most present day hybrids. This long-lived utility bird is bright, alert and quiet. An old Rhody hen makes a good pet, but the cocks are not always so reliable. Legs and feet yellow, eyes red, feathers lustred and glossy mahogany, I prefer the shape of the female, like our cover girl. Mr Potter* who breeds a darker strain of brown at Weybread in Norfolk says they are deservedly popular and good value.

WYANDOTTE
(see p 112)
United States
9lb - 4.08kg

Graceful, but short and deep bodied with a nice shape, Wyandottes are close feathered, pretty and plump, gentle and docile, and available in lots of colours (the laced and pencilled varieties have lost their good laying abilities and the plain colours are getting quite rare). Named after a Native American tribe, they are very beautiful, possibly the most attractive plumage of all. I tried to do a tapestry cushion once of a laced Wyandotte and nearly went cross-eyed. I'm told they are nice natured, make good mums and broodies but the more exotic varieties have become very expensive. They lay a tinted egg and have a rose comb.

SPRING GARDEN SALAD WITH OEUFS MOLLETS AND SPICES

When your hens are laying well in April and everything is shooting up in the potager - but there is not much of any one crop, make this mixed salad for a light lunch or supper.

4 handfuls of mixed salad leaves
Baby spinach, sorrel, chard, corn salad, purslane etc
20 or so leaves of buckler-leaf sorrel*
4 -6 eggs
1 teaspoon cumin seed
1 teaspoon coriander seed
1 teaspoon sesame seeds
Coarse sea salt & black pepper
4 tablespoons extra virgin olive oil

Tear the leaves coarsely if large, or leave whole and arrange on 4 white plates. Place the buckler-leaf sorrel leaves around the edge. Put the eggs in boiling water and cook for six minutes. Shell carefully under running water and keep warm. Toast the seeds in a dry non-stick frying pan until they smell aromatic, tip them into a mortar, add salt and pepper and crush all together lightly. Halve the eggs, place on the salad leaves and sprinkle with the spice mixture. Warm the olive oil in the frying pan, and pour, sizzling over the salads. Serve immediately with olive or walnut bread.

Rhode Island Red Hen

Silver Grey Dorking Cock

COCKERELS

You don't have to keep a cock with your hens to get eggs.

I admire my cockerel, respecting his role as leader of his troupe of ladies. He is usually firm but fair, endlessly diligent and paternal. He keeps a watchful eye open and allows his hens to feed first (this politeness wanes a little outside the breeding season). I have never experienced one who was aggressive to humans. But if a cockerel ever tries to attack you, pick him up immediately in a firm but kind way and stroke him gently, making sure he understands who is boss. If he repeats his bad behaviour, he may have to go. He could be dangerous, especially to children.

My present incumbent - though handsome and solicitous to most of his wives - has taken against one old lady who now spends her time with us in the house or patrolling the boundaries of the garden. He is highly sexed and over-eggs the pudding. I'm tempted to buy a saddle for his wives to protect their sides from his spurs (available from the Domestic Fowl Trust*). My friend Annabel is convinced that though efficient in protecting her hens' flanks, the saddle was less useful when the fox came to visit.

Examining a stressed hen recently, I was horrified to find a huge gash down her side caused by the cockerel's burgeoning spurs. I cleaned her wound with salt water and isolated her safely. Grabbing the culprit and following instructions in an old poultry manual, my husband set to with a hacksaw. The cockerel didn't flinch, but the book failed to mention the spur contained an artery. The sight of my poor cockerel goose-stepping away with blood coursing down his leg is one I shall never forget. It didn't seem to dampen his ardour either, but he has improved with age. To correctly blunt the spurs on your cockerel, use a small hacksaw to take off the *point* and then smooth the rough edges with a nail file or heavy-duty emery board. (See overleaf). Cocks with large combs, like Leghorns sometimes suffer from frostbite in the winter. You can prevent this by smearing the comb with Vaseline.

What to do with excess cockerels? This is the only downside to keeping chickens. You have several options. I know it's possible to run two flocks if you have the space. I have a friend with a boundless garden who keeps two different worlds of hens. I can't believe they don't realize the other exists, but they've never met and everyone is happy, but remember - the more hens you have, the bigger the toll they take on your garden. In some cases a subsidiary cockerel will adopt a secondary role. He won't crow, he'll be slow to develop male characteristics, and will generally try to keep as low a profile as possible. A cockerel can take over a year to develop fully, but sooner or later, usually as the dominant fellow starts to age, the pretender will usurp power and annexe his wives, and terrible battles take place - sometimes to the death, and the hens get stressed and pestered.

Occasionally you can find a home for a good pure breed. All flocks need some new blood every two or three years, so ask around. Some people take spare cocks to market and find a suitable customer. Some people just drive them out to the middle of nowhere, not at all recommendable. Or you have to cull them. In the country you may find a local butcher, breeder or gamekeeper who will do the deed, and you could learn from watching him how to do this yourself. I have never been able to. I know I'm imperfect.

Having killed them, do you eat them? This is out of the question as far as I'm concerned. I wouldn't eat other family pets, however palatable, but some feel that domestic animals are raised to feed people and having lived good but short lives are destined for the pot. There *is* something noble about animals raised well for slaughter. It is a traditional part of country life, a livelihood as old as the countryside itself and one still fulfilled with pride by a few farmers who cherish and love their livestock. I encourage their survival and eat their produce, and wish them success in the face of battery and factory farming.

You may be tempted to show a handsome bird at a poultry show. Contact the Breeds Club of your particular fancy and check out the system first, get to know the terminology, ask for a list of points, visit and chat to other contestants. Raising, breeding and grooming showbirds is a world apart; they must be kept out of the sun to protect their plumage and feeding can include anything from tinned catfood to cake dipped in sherry. A friend who had shown her eggs locally for years, was seduced by a favourite Silkie to enter him. She was reduced to tears by a couple of old boys who ridiculed her cockerel's 'saddle'. Although all the people I've met from the Poultry Club of Great Britain* have been helpful and charming, (the high spot of 1999 was a visit from their President the Reverend Ray Trudgian and his wife), at a village level, small clubs can very occasionally be unwelcoming to newcomers. Especially - dare I say it - to ladies.

MAY
Timely Advice

○ Order chick crumbs from your feed merchant.

○ Cover any seedlings or new plantings with cloches or cages.

○ Protect lower leaves of runner beans until they've grown up out of reach.

○ When your chicks are a week old, prop up the bottom of the coop so mum and chicks can get in and out and explore while the other hens are out in the garden or in the other half of the run.

○ Stake or cloche any vulnerable plants.

○ Cover the base of shrubs with pebbles if a dustbath has been started.

○ Keep the cock segregated if he is pestering his wives. Let him into the garden if they are in the run or vice versa.

○ If your cock's crowing is driving you or the neighbours mad, he could spend nights in a large, well-ventilated box in an outhouse or garage.

○ Search for missing hens - could be sitting broody in a hedge somewhere.

MARANS
(see p 32)
France
8lb - 3.60kg

Prolific layer of nice brown eggs (and the British like a brown egg). The Marans has not been overbred so its utility characteristics have been preserved for fear of losing the egg's colour. With red eyes, white feet and dark cuckoo plumage, the markings though not spectacular, are elegant. There are also less common silver, golden cuckoo and shiny black Marans. Imported to this country in the 1930s from France (the English and French have traditionally, as in all things, been healthily competitive on the poultry front), Marans are easy, active, disease resistant, and prepared to rough it. Leslie Geddes-Brown who runs a flock of Marans in her formal Suffolk garden designed by George Carter, says she has always kept them for their deep brown eggs and because they are placid, pleasant and housewifely.

58

LEGHORN
(see p 61)
Italy
7.5lb 3.40kg

With a racy streamlined body by Ferrari, the Leghorn comes in 10 colours, including Exchequer, (black and white) silver duckwing, and pyle (mulitcoloured) - there are 23 varieties in the States, where most of the modern breeding has been done. The Leghorn is recognizable by its huge red comb, upright in cocks and tipping saucily over to one side on females and is named after the Italian town of Livorno. It has long wattles, and white earlobes so lays white eggs. Active and sprightly, like all Mediterranean fowl Leghorn hens lay well. I love the outline and think it looks best in solid colours. Americans traditionally don't like brown eggs, thinking them dirty, so Leghorns are very popular Stateside and form the basis of many laying hybrids that produce pure white eggs.

WARM POTATO AND EGG SALAD WITH SORREL MAYONNAISE

One of the best uses for really fresh eggs is to make proper mayonnaise - it won't curdle if you take it slowly. If you want a thick, yellow ointment use just the yolks, but adding a whole egg makes a lighter-textured mayonnaise which is better as a base for other flavours: mustard, watercress or sorrel.

1 egg plus 1 yolk at room temperature
1 teaspoon Dijon Mustard
9 fl oz/250ml sunflower or light olive oil
Juice of 1/2 lemon or 1 teaspoon white wine or tarragon vinegar
Salt and pepper

Break the egg into a small bowl and add the egg yolk, mustard and a teaspoon of lemon juice or vinegar. Stand the bowl on a damp J cloth (to stop it sliding around) and beat the ingredients together with a small wire whisk. Have the oil in a jug and start adding it drop by drop with a fork, while whisking continuously. After a while the mixture forms a thick emulsion. Now you can add the oil more quickly, pouring in a slow, steady stream - keep whisking until all the oil is amalgamated. Taste and season, adding more lemon juice or vinegar to balance the oiliness of the mayonnaise.

To make a quick Spring salad, add a few very finely chopped sorrel leaves to 3 tablespoons of mayonnaise and 2 tablespoons of yogurt. Stir together and spoon over a dish of warm, cooked waxy salad potatoes and quartered hard-boiled eggs, on a bed of lettuce leaves. Ribbon slice a few more sorrel leaves as a garnish and serve immediately.

Exchequer Leghorn Cockerel

Lavender Araucana Hen

CHICKEN FEED

Hens are omnivores and will thrive on a basic diet of grain plus their harvest from the wide-open spaces of your garden. If you expect them to lay throughout the year however, they'll need more protein than is available from worms (even though they're 90% protein), grubs, and flies to lay to their full potential. Good, short grass is rich in protein.

Most people offer pellets. The ingredients' list on the packaging of animal feeds is notoriously uninformative. Traditionally they contain animal protein - anything from feathers to bones, meat to droppings, often waste products of other industries. Try to find those that are soya based. Marriages* or Allen and Page* offer the best, including non-GM ingredients and added omega oils. Contact them for stockists or ask your feed merchant to supply you. The taste of the eggs will be affected by what your hens eat, so it won't be your imagination if eggs from birds fed on fishmeal taste a little fishy.

If you watch freerange birds as they busy about your garden, you'll discover the true meaning of the word 'omnivore'. A little greenery, a peck of grit, a worm or two and a couple of woodlice; then a drop of dew trapped in an alchemilla leaf, a little compost, and a few seeds; a fly, some grass, the odd petal, all disappear in staccato pecks while the legs carry on at a stately progress. This of course, is not to mention virtually anything that is green or takes their fancy from salad and brassica leaves to whole mice and sorrel or rhubarb. All is ground in the gizzard with the help of small stones and flints, then passed on through the gut - a truly magnificent apparatus.

The menu *chez nous* makes this a many starred hen café. With moistened brown bread and sunflower hearts* in the run for breakfast; a few sweetcorn kernels and cheap cheese with leftover rice or pasta when the cockerel brings his troupe to the kitchen door for a snack, and a large scoop of mixed corn last thing at night. (Don't encourage your flock to spend all day at the kitchen door waiting for food though, it's better they forage or they'll get too fat and stop laying.)

Apparently hens don't 'taste' food but are aware of texture, so the way to introduce a new food is to partly mix it with the old, gradually increasing quantities until the changeover is complete. Mine have never liked pellets, but love leftover porridge on a cold morning, so occasionally I mix in a little mashed pellet. I don't give my hens crushed eggshells because I'm not keen they should get ideas about eating eggs.

While your hens have access to vast expanses of garden, field or orchard, the food you offer is not a matter of life or death. But if for some reason they are confined to the run, it is essential you offer a mixed diet. Give them bulk in the form of cereal. Mixed corn is best, (though some people swear by wheat alone - a good evening feed slowly digested throughout the night); greenery as grass, brassicas or lettuce; protein pellets for breakfast and mixed grit from your feed merchant and plenty of clean water. For treats offer fruit, nuts, raisins, seeds or cheese and bacon rind. Don't give citrus fruit, salt or sugar, meat or fish (although these would be wolfed down, it's a bad idea and will attract rats).

You can scatter corn on the ground, but pellets need to be kept dry or they'll go mouldy. I prefer galvanized drinkers and feeders to plastic. You'll soon find out what kitchen scraps are acceptable - I suspect the malodorous saucepans of chicken food of my youth, potato peelings simmered for hours would get short shrift from my flock. Start as you mean to go on. Hens are creatures of habit and don't like sudden changes in diet or routine.

During the moult or when it's cold and wet I sometimes give my hens poultry spice* dissolved in warm water and mixed with bread. Researching in old chicken books I often saw advertisements and read their extravagant claims. I was surprised recently to come across a tin and phoned their chemist to find out about the ingredients. It contains magnesium, potassium, calcium, iron, ash, and spices. The rich yellow colour comes from fenugreek and turmeric, described in Lesley Bremness' book the 'Handbook of Herbs'* as uterine and sexual stimulants, with benefits for post natal and period problems and valued in veterinary medicine by the Arabs, Egyptians, Greeks, Indians and Romans. No wonder it's eaten with such gusto.

Open a chicken café and you'll get other diners. Some, like the flock of corn buntings that arrive in the summer are welcome. Others, like the pigeons who complete their meal with a snack from the vegetable garden are not. My cat frightens them off, but Troston is the pigeon capital of the world. Discourage other vermin by clearing up surplus food and keeping feed in a metal dustbin.

JUNE
Timely Advice

○ Take special care of your chicks - mother will be starting to lose interest and they will be more confident and inquisitive.

○ Cover asparagus with black nylon netting - some hens rather like asparagus.

○ Make lots of low cages for the salad garden.

○ Plant out vegetable and salad seedlings started in pots in the greenhouse.

○ Net strawberries, all birds love strawberries.

○ Make sure your hens have access to plenty of shady spots.

○ Join a poultry club and visit their annual show.

○ Relax in the garden with your flock. I'm sure it all looks wonderful.

WELSUMMER
(see p 22)
Holland
7lb - 3.20kg

Developed in Holland in the late 1920s for its large brown egg - sometimes covered in spots and speckles, the Welsummer combines laying merits with subtle beauty, especially the hen with her delicate partridge markings and compact body shape. Upright, alert and active, with yellow legs, bright red combs and large wattles, the cockerel looks like the Kelloggs' cock. There is also a less common Silver duckwing variety. Mr and Mrs Fenning* who breed prize-winning Welsummers near Ipswich, say they are a decorative medium-sized breed that is docile, lays a moderate amount of spectacular eggs and would do well in the garden.

ARAUCANA
(see p 62)
Chile
7lb - 3.20kg

Indiginous to Chile, Araucanas were the last South American breed to be integrated with the Spanish invaders' domestic fowl. Available in a wide range of colours and patterns, these are strange looking birds with orange eyes, thick muffling around the head, and pea combs. Penny Hands keeps them for their pretty tinted eggs. The colour goes right through the shell and can range through tinted to green to blue, getting paler as the year wanes. With a strange topknot, a muff and a beard, you can get lavender, duckwing, pyle, crele, spangled, or cuckoo birds. The Araucana is an active breed, with olive, or willow coloured legs, and a deep, compact body. Though very decorative, they are energetic foragers, are easy to keep and cope well with the English climate. There is also a rumpless version.

69

SAFFRON AND HONEY CUSTARDS

These intensely coloured and delicately flavoured little baked custards make a luxurious and indulgent end to a special meal.

³/₄ pt/400ml single cream
Large pinch (¹/₄ teaspoon) saffron filaments
4 large egg yolks
2oz/60g honey

Crush the saffron filaments and sprinkle them on the cream in a saucepan. Bring the cream to boiling point, then leave to infuse for 10-15 minutes.

Beat the egg yolks and honey together in a basin and whisk in the cream. Put the basin over a saucepan of simmering water and cook gently until the custard coats the back of a metal spoon. Pour into four ramekins and place them in a roasting tin, adding hot water to come about an inch up the sides. Bake in a low oven 275F/130C for about an hour until just set. Serve warm or cool with sharp cooked fruit such as rhubarb or apricots.

Eggs are rich in vitamin B12 - good for the nervous and circulatory systems and also in vitamin D that helps the body absorb calcium, essential for strong teeth and bones.

Store eggs in a cold larder or in a fridge, but remember to remove them half an hour before use to bring them back to room temperature.

Baked Honey and Saffron Custard

Welsummer, Araucana, Leghorn and Orpington Eggs

EGGS

The egg is a perfect natural food; unrefined, unprocessed and unenriched - the most versatile ingredient in your larder. But since commercial poultry must be the most abused food commodity, how can their eggs offer us any sustenance at all? As Juliette de Baïracli Levy writes in her book Complete Herbal for Farm and Stable*: 'Scientific analysis may prove such eggs to have minerals and vitamins, but science fails badly in nutrition'. You *know* your hens' eggs are far superior to a commercial egg. I recently made a dish demanding 12 whole eggs. It was October, I could only muster six. The remaining half dozen supermarket organic freerange eggs looked palely up at me out of the bowl, instantly recognizable, in a second rate way by their paper shells, watery whites and funny smell.

Standard hens lay eggs that weigh about 65grams and a bantam egg weighs about 40. There is plenty of variation within this scale depending on breed, age and time of the year. You may find tiny 'cocks' eggs that often don't have a yolk, and huge double yolkers that have two. A young hen may lay a little egg to start with, then she'll lay smallish eggs throughout her first year; in the second & third year her eggs will get bigger and then in her fourth and fifth year you'll get some whoppers. From then on her laying season will get shorter as she grows older. My Nellie laid 40 eggs in her ninth and final year. Occasionally, you'll find a soft-shelled egg, or a strange shaped one. If these persist it's worth checking your birds' diet and adding oyster shell,* but I find it's usually a temporary blip.

Eggs can be shades of brown, white or blue. Welsummers, Marans and Barnevelders lay dark brown eggs. Leghorns, Minorcas and any hens with white earlobes lay white eggs; Croad Langshans lay plum coloured ones and

Araucanas lay pale blue/green. Most of the others lay lovely tinted eggs, but the colour of the egg's shell makes no difference to the flavour of the egg. That is affected by what your hen eats. The colour of the yolk is determined in nature by the amount of greenery the hen consumes, in batteries by yellow dye added to their feed. If hens are deprived of the right food there will be no eggs at all. They don't lay during the moult because all the protein they eat is used to produce new feathers.

The egg passes slowly through the hen's reproductive system adding albumen, shell, pigment and membrane and then goes quickly through her oviduct and out. Collect eggs every day otherwise she will build up a clutch and go broody. The egg contains the germ plus any food needed by the embryo during incubation and for two days after hatching. Eggs can withstand the weight of a 3 kilo hen from the outside but by hatching time are brittle enough for the chick to peck its way out. The shell is porous so they shouldn't be stored next to food that smells. Don't wash or soak eggs to clean them, just wipe with a loofah or scourer dampened in warm water. If you suspect a hen is eating eggs, a clutch of ping-pong balls will sometimes do the trick, but prompt collection is the best deterrent. Magpies, stoats, mink and ferrets will take eggs. I've even heard of pet dogs regularly stealing and eating them. Many people are worried that if they keep a cock with their hens, they may be confronted with nasty surprises every time they tap open their breakfast egg. It's true the egg will be fertile, worth remembering if you have dietary or religious qualms, but until it has been under a broody, there will be only the tiniest red speck of difference between a fertile and a non-fertile egg. Date your eggs with a soft pencil, collect them every day and eat them fresh.

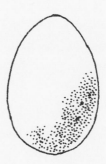

To find out about selling surplus eggs, phone your local Ministry of Ag. Fish and Food office for their latest deliberations on the subject. If you want organic ones you'll have to garden organically and make sure everything you feed your hens is organic. Birds lay more in Spring and Summertime because there is more natural food and more daylight to find it in. If you want eggs out of season, you have to supply more protein and light. Like us, birds need food for energy, warmth and the repair of new cells. It's the surplus food that provides the eggs.

Our image of peasant cottagers with hens pecking round their backyard, encourages us to fondly imagine that their families were enjoying nice little boiled eggs regularly for breakfast and that their paltry diet was thus daily enriched. Sadly though, lack of adequate protein allowed the hens to lay just once in springtime and then hatch out a brood. The surviving pullets were then duly eaten by the owner. Better the occasional meal of scraggy chicken, than the daily egg.

As a member of the New Peasantry, I find I get the least eggs in October, but by November/December the new pullets are coming into lay, and the next youngest birds come on in mid February. Maximum production is in March and April. May is not so good because my hens seem to be perpetually broody, but then they settle down. The rest of the year's output is interrupted by moulting individuals, but there are still more than enough eggs for us all.

Six best pure breed layers:

Rhode Island Red	260 tinted eggs p a
Sussex	260 tinted eggs
Fayoumi	250 tinted eggs
Leghorn	240 white eggs
Friesian	230 white eggs
Marans	200 brown eggs

JULY
Timely Advice

- During heatwaves make sure the henhouse has adequate ventilation.
- If security is a problem, replace open doors with weld mesh panels.
- Clean out the house more frequently in hot weather.
- Start to worry if any chicks look like cockerels.
- Add a teaspoon of Epsom salts to drinking water to give hens a boost.
- If there's a sawfly problem on gooseberries, let hens eat the caterpillars.
  Make sure there are no ripe windfalls or they'll eat the berries too.
- Re-fill drinkers more frequently during hot spells.
- Make lots of icecream for the freezer with surplus eggs and soft fruit.

APPENZELLER SPITSHAUBEN
(see p 11)
Switzerland
4.5lb - 2kg

I've included this breed simply because I think it is very beautiful. They remind me of *fin de siècle* Prussian ladies and military gentlemen, possibly astride white *Lippizzaner* horses. Spangled in black and gold or black and white with a grey fluffy undercarriage, serious combs and a topknot, Appenzellers have beady black eyes and smart grey legs. It is a breed I know little about and have always admired in books, but Jane Lee keeps lots of chickens and these are her favourites. The nicest natured, even in crosses, her strain is friendly. She would recommend them for children, but they are expensive. Delicate looking though really quite hardy, but when I asked her what colour the eggs were, she couldn't remember - (they are white, small and infrequent).

SILKIE
(see p 12)
China
4lbs - 1.81kg

Reportedly seen by Marco Polo on his travels in China. Best broodies of all on any eggs, especially a Silkie cross. Available in black, blue, gold, white and partridge, the hens look like Anna Karenina in winter finery. Soft with really silky, fluffy hair-like feathers, a charming bird to keep as a pet. The earlobes are turquoise or mulberry coloured, with a slate grey beak and shiny black eyes. It's an adaptable little bird whose black skin, flesh and bones have saved it from the table. Though decorative and fragile-looking, it is hardy and lays well when not broody. It is susceptible to scaly leg and has five toes. My friend Linda has a flock of four and says they are easy and undemanding, stick close to the house - even though these have access to a large garden and strangely enough hers rarely go broody.

LIGHT SCONES

Anyone can make good scones with this recipe - try them with jam, honey or homemade Lemon Curd (the recipe is on page 20).

8oz/250g self-raising flour with a pinch of salt
1½oz/50g caster sugar
3oz/100g butter at room temperature, cubed
1 large egg
Buttermilk or plain yogurt

Preheat the oven to 450F/220C and lightly grease a baking sheet.

Sift the flour and salt into a warm bowl and add the sugar. Then rub in the butter lightly with your fingertips until the mixture looks like coarse breadcrumbs. Break the egg into a measuring jug, beat with a fork and then add buttermilk or yogurt to bring the mixture up to the 5fl oz/150ml level. Beat together and then pour into the bowl and mix with a palette knife until the dough comes together. It should be slightly sticky, so add a little more liquid if it looks dry. Knead lightly with floured hands, then pat it onto a floured surface to 1"/2.5cm thick.

Flour a 2"/5cm cutter and cut out rounds, placing them on the baking sheet. Re-form and cut the trimmings. Dust the tops with flour and bake them in the top of the oven for 10-12 minutes. If you can lift one without the top breaking off, they are done. Put them on a wire cooling rack and wrap the whole thing in a tea towel. Ideally - serve while still warm.

For fruit scones add 2oz/60g mixed dried fruit, sultanas or chopped, peeled eating apple to the mixture after rubbing in the butter.

Barbu D'Uccles Millefleur Hen

Nellie the Broody and Chick

CHICKS

Many years ago I met a breeder who was convinced that hens (being closely related to reptiles) could be persuaded by cooler temperatures to hatch out more females in colder summers, like crocodiles do. He experimented with incubator heat to try to get more hens. He also thought that late hatchings resulted in more hens. It may have just been luck, but for the last four autumns I have hatched hens. This year, a wet one with generally poor fertility, resulted in one heatwave-hatched September chick - now a fine cockerel. Obviously an inexact science. Luckily I've found him a home.

Because I only set a few Orpington eggs each year, often only one chick hatches. She has the total attention and protection of her mother. Probably like most 'only' offspring, life's not much fun, but she is gradually integrated into the flock by eight weeks. She's at the bottom of the pecking order, but come the early winter she will start laying and then her status will improve with the cock's 'interest'.

Poultry lovemaking is a lacklustre affair. Where on earth have all the sexual connotations come from? (The mallard drake is a far more rampant creature). Cocks don't even have a phallus, just a groove that channels the semen into the hen's vagina. All you'll see is the Cockerel moving towards the hen, she crouches (or runs off *very* fast), he mounts her and treads her back, grasping her head with his beak. He then dismounts. She'll shake herself and move away. He only *needs* to perform once per brood to fertilize a whole clutch and she's born with thousands of egg germs waiting to be released one at a time. Fertile eggs stay viable for two weeks (to be on the safe side) and if they are put under a broody or incubated, they should hatch.

A broody hen is unmistakable - fluffed up, clucking and rigid if disturbed, she wants to stay on the nest, even if there are no eggs for her to sit on. If you decide not to use her, remove any eggs and just leave her to rest for three weeks, taking her off the nest daily and offering her food and drink. You could try shutting her out of the nest box for a while. She *may* give up.

If you decide to go ahead and hatch, wait a few days until she is completely settled and then, in the evening move her to a ready-prepared broody house with a sod of turf on the floor. Make a slight depression in the middle, add a little straw round the edge and place the eggs you want to hatch in the middle. Only set perfect eggs. Discard any irregular, elongated, pocked, mottled, or very dirty ones. They should be the right size for the hen that laid them - outsize or miniature eggs will not be viable. Some say an even number is best, some say odd and I've even heard people promoting eggs laid in the new moon. Pop her on top of the clutch, keeping the door shut until she has settled and then leave her to get on with it. If she doesn't nip out regularly for food, drink and ablutions, you may have to lift her daily.

A broody turns her eggs every two hours. When you lift her you'll find a small bare patch on her breast where she's plucked her feathers so the eggs have contact with her warm flesh. Inside the egg the cell has divided and the heart, wings, head and brain are developing and by day 15 the chick is tiny, but complete. By this time make sure the house is surrounded by a coop covered with small gauge nylon net with a board on top offering shelter from the elements.

Check that there is water in the chick drinker* (or upturned flowerpot in a saucer so they don't drown) and if you decide to feed chick crumbs, that you have some ready for the new arrivals. By day 18-19 there is movement and cheeping inside the egg and the yolk has been absorbed. All this happens simultaneously in all the eggs you set, so do not introduce any more to the clutch from day one or allow other hens to lay in the nest at a later date.

On the 20/21 day, a small hole appears at the broad end of the egg and between 6 to 10 hours later, tired and exhausted, the chick hatches. But she (hopefully it's a she) isn't hungry or thirsty, she has absorbed enough nourishment in the egg to survive for 2 days. Leave the chick and mum to relax and any siblings to emerge. After two days the hen will lead her family out and you can remove the old nest - and any unhatched eggs and eggshells. If she stays sitting on eggs, take them away. Don't forget to feed her. Keep them all in the coop separate from the rest of the flock for the first week, letting them out into the main run after the others have gone into the garden. Prop up the bottom of the coop with a brick so the brood can come back and shelter if necessary. Some hybrids, like first generation Rhodebars and Legbars can be sexed now because the males are a different colour.

If you want to hatch birds in an incubator, I suggest you read Dr Batty's book *Artificial Incubation**. I only have one incubated bird, a beautiful Black Orpington. I love her dearly, but she just isn't very clever - not as streetwise as the rest of my hens, but that could just be the breed. Prone to small infections (she's not immune to the particular illnesses present in our terrain or local bird population), she poses like Scarlett O'Hara in her black taffeta standing on the steps at Tara, with grey feet and painted toenails.

Feed the chicks four times a day on meals of shredded raisins and lettuce, mashed peas, ground sunflower hearts, moistened wholemeal bread, pin oatmeal mixed with cod liver oil, or any poultry food ground in an old coffee grinder. Finely chopped garlic can be added to prevent worms. Some people give chicks chopped hard-boiled eggs; that doesn't seem quite right somehow. Mum will teach them what to eat and what things - like wasps, to avoid. She'll show them how to dustbathe, scratch and forage, calling them for food in the same tone as the cock calls his ladies.

Gradually reduce the number of feeds. The hen will stay with her family for six to eight weeks. She'll sleep with them on the floor and then go back to the main house with the rest of the flock. She smoothes down her feathers like an instant post-natal diet, and the chicks no longer recognize her slimmed-down silhouette. Nature severs the tie - instant adolescence. The pullets can stay in a separate house, but reduce the size of the pophole with a piece of cut cardboard, so the bigger birds can't get in and bully them. By 12 to 14 weeks the cockerels will be obvious by their pointed neck and saddle feathers and by 18 weeks both will be fully fledged.

AUGUST
Timely Advice

- If you are going on holiday, organize a hensitter to come in twice a day to feed your hens, change their water and collect the eggs.
- Consider buying an automatic feeder* to make life easier, but human supervision is still essential.
- If there is evidence of mites add some powder* to the dustbathing site.
- Make sure your growing pullets are fed protein.
- Take time to relax with your birds in the shade.

BARBU D'UCCLES
(see p 81)
Belgium
30oz - 910g

Known in this country as Ducals, this Belgian bantam has a single comb, tiny wattles, a little beard and feathery legs, with stiff hock feathers sticking out to the side at right angles, like Charlie Chaplin's feet. Full fronted and puffed out like a pigeon with hackles, this breed comes in Millefleur (spotty), Porcelain (delicate pastel shades), Cuckoo (Striped), and Mottled varieties (15 in the States). The hens are quiet and cobby and the males are sporty They are easy to breed, and hardy, unlike other tiny bantams, but D'Uccles need plenty of shelter from the weather. Really only bred for show or as pets, do not expect much in the egg department.

BARBU D'ANVERS
(see p 91)
Belgium
28oz - 790g

Referred to as Danvers, they are ornamental natural bantams, having no standard variation. Small, standing boldly upright, like a proud little Flemish merchant in a red cap, not out of place in a Breughel painting. The face is large, whiskery and owl-like, with a relatively big curved beak. They are clean legged, and speedy with a tiny red comb and no wattles. The cock's wings point down almost to the ground and the hen is plump and lively. Easy for beginners, D'Anvers are reasonable layers in spring and summer months. Stephen Flory breeds both these little Belgian birds (along with many others) at the Henhouse at Thorndon in Suffolk* and finds them endearing, busy, and easy, but warns the tiny cockerels can be fiery.

SCENTED GERANIUM LEAF ICE CREAM

Not all scented geranium, (pelargoniums) are suitable for this recipe. The best are the rose or lemon-rose scented ones, such as Attar of Roses and Lady Plymouth. Don't use the supposedly apple-scented Pelargonium Odorissimum - it smells and tastes exactly like cheap soap.

4fl oz/125ml milk
8 leaves scented geranium (more if small)
12fl oz/375ml whipping cream
2 large egg yolks
3¹/₂oz/100g vanilla sugar

Wash and dry the geranium leaves. Put them in a stainless steel saucepan with the milk and cream and bring to boiling point. Remove from the heat, cover and leave to infuse for 10-15 minutes. Taste and leave a little longer if the flavour has not developed - remember that freezing dulls the flavour. In a heatproof bowl combine egg yolks and sugar and whisk together till pale and moussey. Strain the flavoured milk mixture into the bowl, beating until amalgamated. Place the bowl over a pan of simmering water and cook very gently, stirring until the mixture coats the back of a metal spoon. Stand the basin in cold water immediately and leave it to get cold, stirring occasionally to avoid a skin forming. Cover with cling film and chill in the fridge. Freeze in an ice cream maker for 15-25 minutes until the mixture has the consistency of whipped cream. Scrape into a plastic box and leave in the deep freeze for at least an hour. If frozen solid, move to the fridge for 20 minutes before serving - with strawberries and little biscuits perhaps.

Instead of geranium leaves, you could infuse a handful of rose petals, a few lavender flower sprigs or some angelica leaves in the cream mixture.

Barbu D'Anvers Quail Hen

Gold Sebright Cock

NEWCOMERS

Whether you are buying your first hens or augmenting an existing flock - (and I've been unable to convince you to hatch your own), you must decide now what breed you would like by studying the form. Look here in the Breeds chapter, consult the Poultry Standards book* at the library or visit Poultry Club Shows.* Decisions made, look locally first, try asking feed merchants and vets, and read the local papers. You'll make some good contacts and meet some fascinating people; small-scale breeders who will try to convince you of the charms of their fancies. Don't buy from markets. No-one sends their best birds to market. Give yourself plenty of time, you may have to order and wait for eggs to hatch or chicks to grow.

If nothing comes up then contact the Breed Club* of your choice and they will put you in touch with a local breeder. Alternatively write to one of the suppliers* in the directory section. If you are buying from a proper breeder it's worth learning the jargon, otherwise you may get a surprise on receipt of your order. A *pair* is a male and a female - a *trio* is a male and two females. *Hen* is a female after first moult. She is a *pullet* till then. *Chick* is both sexes up to eight weeks. Young male is a *cockerel*, after that he is a *cock*. *Standard* breeds are divided into light and heavy. *Bantams* are miniature standards. Pekins, Silkies, Sebrights are *small breeds* with no standard version.

When collecting your birds, select those with a healthy glow. They should be sleek, well-wattled and tail furnishings should be plentiful. Choose fowl with bright eyes and red combs - too pale could indicate anemia, too dark could augur heart problems. Check for dry nostrils, shiny feathers and no wheezing. Birds from big breeders come ready-vaccinated, but they won't have the built-in immunities that a hatchling from your own brood has. *Caveat emptor*, choose a local breeder so if there are problems, you can go back for help.

Your purchases should be at least 20 weeks old if they are to be introduced to an existing flock. Younger birds will have to be kept in a separate run until they can hold their own. Don't be tempted by chicks - however pretty, unless you have a broody you know will accept them. Whatever aged birds you bring in they must spend several days in *purdah*, cooped separately inside the run so the occupants can get used to each other little by little. It's quite likely the newcomers will have been kept in a cage by their breeder and may find your wide-open spaces a little daunting. I think it kinder to buy in twos, so there's at least one friendly face.

It can take ages for a new bird to be fully accepted so keep an eye on her. If a particular hen is doing the bullying, you could try cooping *her* and letting the victim run with the others. There's always a pecking order in a flock, but with lots of room, places to hide and other things to do, it should only be a problem at mealtimes. Let the newcomer dine alone for a while.

Kept safe in your garden with you around, your flock will thrive. Your hens' main enemies apart from foxes will be uncontrolled dogs. Let your neighbours with dogs know you are keeping expensive birds and would appreciate their co-operation. Family cats are not usually a problem - hens can be formidable opponents, one peck is usually lesson enough, although next door's huge tom could take bantams and chicks. Your own dog can be trained, though terriers and lurchers may prove a bit of a challenge. Other animals that will prey on small, unprotected birds include escapee mink and ferrets, birds of prey, magpies, squirrels, and rats. A covered and well-constructed run with small gauge netting will protect your flock. Always respond to your birds' alarm calls. There's usually good reason.

When you collect your newcomers or if you need to take birds to the vet, transport them in a large cardboard box with plenty of ventilation holes. It is amazing how much heat a few hens can produce. A friend nearly lost a box of Brahmas on the short journey back from the breeder. I prefer a hamper-style or cat basket placed on newspaper on the back seat of the car, rather than in an airless boot. Your hens will go to sleep if the light is reduced. On long journeys stop and water them every few hours. Those who show poultry often give them a boost of soluble multivitamins called Intervits.* A little honey added to a bread and water meal is also a good restorative. We took some Brahmas and Pekins to an RHS show, five hours in a Hillbilly truck. They reacted better then I did and were laying the next day. If you are moving house (Amtrak and British Rail no longer carry livestock), put them in their house (if compact) on the removal van or a trailer. There is a gentleman called Mr. Francis* who will transport and deliver birds in his specially designed van, complete with extractor fan and special lighting.

SEPTEMBER

Timely Advice

- Give your flock a boost during the moult with poultry spice and protein.

- Never clip wings during the moult.

- Let your birds into the vegetable garden to clear the land and eat the veg.

- Protect autumn salads and brassicas with cages.

- Go to collect any new birds, checking they are fit and healthy.

- You may have to buy in eggs. Shop-bought eggs will make you appreciate your hens' efforts. Better buy from a local farm producer.

SEBRIGHT
(see p 92)
United Kingdom
25oz - 620g

Developed in this country two hundred years ago by Sir John Saunders Sebright, these little gold or silver laced birds are difficult to breed and raise as chicks, but adults are hardy, active and like to freerange. Hugh Burton* who breeds them near Cambridge says they like to fly up into trees, so an orchard run would be ideal. They live for eight or nine years. Although not hugely productive they lay tiny white eggs. The cocks can be aggressive and are henfeathered (they don't have pointed neck feathers, so sexing must be done by comb alone). With delicate lacing, not unlike a Wyandotte and a rose comb, they are jaunty, strutting little things, very upright - as though they are trying to look taller. Not recommended for beginners.

PEKIN
(see p 101)
China
24oz - 600g

With their short legs, feathered feet and toes, Pekins (or Cochin bantams as they're called in US) look like little teacosies. An excellent beginner's bird, highly recommended for children, they are very gentle, especially the hens and make good mums. Don't expect regular eggs though. They stick together and seem fond of each other. A wide range of colours: plain black, blue, buff, cuckoo, mottled, barred, columbian, lavender, partridge, white, (16 American varieties). Pekins are tiny birds - all feather. They don't like bad weather, tend not to scratch the flowerbeds and aren't hugely active so don't need much space. Good for a small urban garden, watch out for big cats though. Carol Flory, whose husband bred many of the birds photographed in this book, chooses Pekins as her favourites.

PASTA WITH EGGS, SMOKED GARLIC & FRIED BREADCRUMBS
(This is a vegetarian version of a *Carbonara* sauce).

2 tablespoons olive oil
1 large onion finely sliced
2 cloves smoked garlic finely chopped
2 tablespoons chopped flat parsley
2 eggs
2 tablespoons double cream (optional)
2 tablespoons grated Parmesan or peccorino
2oz/60g butter
8oz/250g spaghetti or other dried pasta
2oz/60g shaved Parmesan or peccorino
Salt and black pepper

Put a pan of water on to boil for the pasta. Heat the olive oil in a frying pan, add the onion and a little salt and cook over a medium heat until soft and beginning to brown. Add the garlic and cook for another minute. Scrape the mixture into a large bowl. In a small bowl, whisk the eggs with the cream (if using) and Parmesan or peccorino. Add the onion mixture and stir in the parsley. Fry the breadcrumbs in butter until they're crisp and brown. Cook the pasta till *al dente*, drain and put in the bowl with the egg and onion mixture. Stir until the egg is just cooked by the heat of the pasta or return to the pan over a gentle heat. Turn the pasta into a warm serving dish and toss with the breadcrumbs, shaved cheese and plenty of black pepper.

You could use smoked cheese and fresh garlic, and for extra piquancy add chopped green or back olives.

Mottled Pekin Cockerel

My Orpington Cockerel in the Kitchen Garden

GARDENS/HENS

I actually garden with my hens. They follow me around, darting between my feet for insects turned over by my trowel. My garden would be a lesser place without them. I know no *serious* gardener would dream of letting hens roam round his precious plot, but I try to be inclusive. This garden, such as it is, survives the combined onslaughts of a flock of ducks, teenage sons with lots of friends, cats, and my hens. And I make my mistakes in public - I'm open to visitors a couple of days a week* for all to see.

I would *never* recommend those with a newly-established garden to let their hens range free, or those who are obsessed with bedding plants or real plantsmen, (although really formal gardens cope well with poultry) but I believe with a little deviousness and a *laissez faire* attitude, it can work. And I do get something back - wonderful fertility, very few pests and the sight of my charming ginger cockerel as he escorts his motley troupe of ladies round the garden.

They say champion compost is made from grass cuttings, human pee and corrugated brown cardboard. Chicken run debris - straw, newspaper, feathers and droppings plus layers of kitchen and garden waste is pretty potent too. Of course you must let the manure rest on the heap and not directly onto plants, but Penny Hands swears by neat chicken droppings on her blackcurrant bushes, so organize a sojourn for the hens in the fruit cage come early winter. Most of the droppings around the garden make their own way into the soil or are dug in. Some are swept up from paths and terraces with leaves. Some are mixed with the lawn mowings and the rest come from the henhouse. All go onto the compost heap, naturally layered with bedding and whatever else is gardened.

I plant catch crops of green manure in my vegetable plot to improve the soil's structure and fertility - plants like alfalfa, comfrey, clover and mustard greens.* Good henfoods all, they need eventually to be dug in, but let your birds feast first, scratch and manure *ad lib*. If your flock has unlimited access to the garden, avoid pesticides, fungicides, herbicides and poisons, especially slug bait and creosote. Hens will make up for this by devouring many of the pests and weed seeds. Mine don't like slugs - who does, but will eat snails if obligingly squashed first. There are poisonous berries, plants, seeds and fungi out there, but somehow poultry seem to know what's what.

In his book Natural Poultry Keeping* Dr. Batty suggests a light or sandy soil suits Leghorns and Orpingtons; a loamy soil is best for Buttercups and Wyandottes; Light Sussex prefer a heavy soil and Anconas and Rhode Island Reds do well on clay. I know that birds with elaborate leg feathers do not appreciate mud, but I think they mostly prefer a nice dry fine tilth. If you confine your birds to their run, (not a bad idea in early Spring when tempting young shoots proliferate), throw all your leftovers, leaves, cuttings, and kitchen waste in there with them. A giant heap to scratch about in will keep them amused and make excellent compost.

In her Herbal* Juliette de Baïracli Levy says that poultry should have access to hawthorn berries, rosehips, beechnuts, weeds and their seeds, wilted nettles, chickweed, fat hen, fennel, dill, peas, lettuce, parsley and linseed - all available in most gardens to be sampled. Hens love an old bonfire site, but make sure there are no sharp objects and obviously no lit cinders lurking underneath. To disperse messes from an otherwise pristine lawn, use a besom or a quick spurt with a high powered hose.

I grow a wide variety of plants, to sell in my shop* and to plant in the garden. So I assume that any that survive - mostly in great profusion and good health - are poultry-proof (one can never be 100% sure, some hens have *very* peculiar tastes). So I can recommend, bearing in mind we are in East Anglia *and* garden on heavy soil: all the euphorbias, the sages, lychnis, stachys, phlomis, ornamental thistles, lavenders, and obviously anything that climbs. Also geraniums, pelargoniums, verbascums, all shrubs and sub-shrubs, marigolds, nasturtiums, love-in-a-mist, pulmonarias and comfreys. Bulbs, arums, daylilies and lilies, hellebores, senecio, violas, most perennial herbs esp. feverfew, acanthus, daisies, helianthus, verbenas, and sedums (if protected when young). Anything vulnerable is planted in a pot or protected with a cloche. My favourites are the Thai bamboo cloches* used in the Far East to coop broodies and chicks.

The cheapest form of protection is a roll of green plastic-coated wire fencing, available in rolls of various heights from garden centres. This can be fashioned into circles and popped over new planting. Lower versions can be turned over inwards to form small cages for plants to grow through (especially good for sedums or anything sappy). In fact, entire beds could be surrounded by this stuff - it virtually disappears as the plants grow up.

Vegetable gardening is more of a problem. Ideally one would have a walled or fenced kitchen garden outlawing rabbits, deer and chickens. Consider the cottager's idea of growing veg tucked away in the front garden. My kitchen garden is accessible to my hens but all salads, brassicas and young plants are covered with 6′ x 4′/2m x 1.25m low netted cages, protecting them from all predators (even Cabbage Whites). Lengths of wired concertina netting tunnels suitable for rows of greenstuff are available from Haxnicks*.

Stop your hens from scratching craters by building a custom-made dustbath in the run or out-of-sight at the back of the border where soil is driest. Some people only let their flocks out in the Autumn, to forage for pests, finish off windfalls plus leftover veg and liberally manure the beds. Extra wild birds will be attracted into your garden by your hens' activity and your flock will create the colour and drama that's missing late in the year. As in all endeavours there'll be the odd mishap, but the seasons will replenish your garden and you'll be compensated with nice eggs and charming companions.

OCTOBER
Timely Advice

- You may have to feed your birds earlier as nights draw in.
- Invest in an automatic feeder for suppers if you are not back in time.
- Wheat is a good evening feed as it is digested slowly.
- Watch out for rats and other vermin.
- Let your flock have access to windfalls and surplus fruit and veg.
- Put duck boards on your route to the run to avoid mud.
- Hope for some frosts to kill germs and pests.
- Leaves dried in paper sacks make good run covering.

Cochin

Orpington

Sussex

Rock

Marans

Leghorn

Appenzeller

Silkie

D'Uccles

Brahma

Dorking

Rhode Island Red

Wyandotte

Welsummer

Araucana

D'Anvers

Sebright

Pekin

WALNUT MACAROONS

Many recipes only need yolk of egg. You can keep spare egg whites in the fridge in a covered bowl for a week or freeze them. One egg white measures about 1fl oz/40ml. Add an extra egg white to a soufflé mixture for even lighter soufflés or make meringues or top fruit tarts with meringue mixture before baking. You can brush uncooked pastry tart shells with egg white to avoid soggy pastry and glaze fruit pies with lightly beaten egg white before sprinkling with caster sugar. But these tasty, chewy biscuits will use up any leftover whites to greater acclaim.

3 large egg whites
3oz/80g golden caster sugar
1$\frac{1}{2}$ teaspoons ground rice
4oz/100g chopped walnuts
Walnut halves to decorate
Rice paper or baking parchment

Pre-heat the oven to 300F/150C.
Arrange sheets of rice paper on two baking trays. Whisk the egg whites with a pinch of salt until really stiff and gradually whisk in the caster sugar. Fold in the ground rice and chopped walnuts and drop the mixture in small heaps on the paper using two spoons. Top each biscuit with a walnut half and bake in the oven for about 30 minutes, changing the trays round after quarter of an hour. The macaroons should be pale brown and firm but still chewy in the middle, and are particularly good served with coffee ice cream.

Walnut Macaroons

Barred Wyandotte Bantam Cock

112

PROBLEMS

If you find a bird that is unwell - hunched up, head down, and eyes closed - isolate her with access to drinking water in a separate henhouse (an old broody house is ideal). Pick her up and hold her. Is she underweight? Feel her crop in her throat, if it is hard, dose her with a little olive oil. Is she straining to lay an egg, again a little oil rubbed round the vent may help. If you are unsure, take her to the vet as soon as you can. You will probably have paid more for her than your cat. Explain she is a family pet and she'll be treated as such. While she's recuperating keep the patient isolated from nasty neighbours who will abuse an ailing bird.

I leave the medicating of my animals to experts. I have never understood why henkeepers are expected to treat their own birds. As though to be able to dispatch a chicken with the flick of a wrist, and indulge in a spot of avian surgery or administer patent nostrums by injection are pre-requisites for a fully-fledged poultryman. If you are a budding Herriot, may I recommend a helpful book by Victoria Roberts - Diseases of Free Range Poultry.* All vets should have a copy, because those that can deal with hens as individuals (as opposed to part of a flock) are as rare as hen's teeth. So are easily administered medicines. Most are prescribed to be diluted in litres of water for thousands of birds, resulting in over-medication, immunity to antibiotics and wasting of eggs. If only remedies were available in tablet form to be hidden in a bit of cheese, or calculated (without a maths degree) to be diluted in small amounts of water, added to bread and hand fed to the patient. When dosing hens with any medicines, throw away all the eggs.

Over the years I've found hens and cocks dead. The Orpingtons die suddenly of heart attacks - they are bred for their size and it can be their undoing.

113

Because they are prey, all chickens hide the fact they're ill, fearful of showing weakness, so often by the time they are exhibiting symptoms, it's too late for you to help them. They can be nasty to weaker members of the flock and left to their own devices in a confined space, pecking and cannibalism are common. As a child, incarcerated in a Belgian convent, our dismal playground was next to the chicken run where birds hopped in and out of giant bovine skeletons, polishing off the carcass' remains and generally being beastly to one another. The nuns were totally self-sufficient and at breakfast we played Russian Roulette with the edibility or otherwise of our boiled eggs (the alternative was dried cured horse-meat, especially for little English girls with ponies at home). So deny your birds wholesome recreation at your peril.

The health and well-being of my flock is hugely important to me. I believe hens - like all of us, are what they eat, and offered a wide freerange menu and a stress-free life, they will thrive. I treat for worms, lice or scaly leg when the need arises, not as a matter of course. If you do notice a bird whose leg and foot scales are risen, flaky and uneven, catch her and dunk the whole leg in a jam jar of surgical spirit. Repeat every week for a month.

Learn to hold your birds correctly. Pass your upturned hand under the hen's breast and grasp her legs with your fingers. Use your other hand to steady and stroke her. You'll find she won't like it much. Being creatures that are preyed on in nature, birds think they are being ambushed, but held regularly they learn to submit in a resigned sort of way. The best time to catch them is from the roost at night, they are relaxed and cornered. If you have to trap a hen in the open, a long handled fishing net is useful or a bamboo cloche. Wear a pair good of gardening gloves and try to appear calm and confident.

All birds moult their feathers (and leg scales) annually. Some hens lose their feathers early, some late - unfortunately it doesn't seem to depend on the weather. Your flock will look like broilers first and then porcupines - because the feathers grow up through a transparent tube that then falls away. The henhouse floor will be covered with bushels of feathers. Unattractive and unlovable, their plumage will be back at its peak in time for Christmas and the breeding season. One drawback to a mixed-age flock is that occasionally a young cockerel that isn't moulting is running with a few old ladies who obviously are. They will want nothing to do with him, so shut him out of the chicken run to pace its confines and leave his wives inside in peace to mope about unseen in various stages of undress. Good layers can go almost naked, dignified by a few feathers stuck in strategic places. Young birds won't moult until their second year and all go egg-less during the moult. There are other reasons for not laying; insufficient protein, broodiness, bullying, vermin, when the hen has chicks and the following eight weeks, lack of light, stress, new surroundings, and illness. Traditionally, the laying season is Valentines Day to Guy Fawkes' night.

If you have to clip her wings (a small hen can flap her way out of a 2 metre run, a large Orpington would need rocket powered assistance) get some help and hold the bird while your assistant trims the first three flight feathers on one wing. The keratin on overgrown beaks and claws that perpetual broodies grow can be carefully trimmed with nail clippers and filed smooth.

One of my first memories as a child, aged two, is of the terrier man coming to rid our run of rats. Keenly interested, I watched the hens lifting their petticoats on the henhouse roof as rats and dogs raced round the coop. Every year harvest and cold weather signal the migration of the rat population from fields to outhouses and gardens. If they're made welcome and find things to eat - henfood is just the ticket - they'll stay. Discourage vermin by storing feed in metal dustbins - with metal lids, and every evening clear away leftovers. Following these precautions I probably have fewer rat problems than neighbours without hens, but I can recommend the Wide Piper* a clever rat-diameter piece of pipe with a see-through bait dispenser, which will keep the poison out of reach of hens and other family pets.

With luck though your hens, like mine, will live long, productive and problem-free lives. And when finally and sadly you come to bury a member of your flock in the garden, (corpses are not appreciated by binmen) bury her four feet deep, so she is not disinterred by scavengers or pets, especially if she has been medicated. You'll find a burst of heavy digging good catharsis for loss, and your hen will benefit the garden one last time.

NOVEMBER/DECEMBER
Timely Advice

- Pullets may start to lay for the first time - first eggs may be tiny.
- Older hens will stop laying.
- Some hens moult late, make sure the henhouse is ready for winter.
- Let your flock range in as many parts of the garden as possible.
- Check they have access to shelter from the wind and rain.
- If you have a bonfire, hens love ashes to dustbathe, check there are no hot cinders. Obviously they won't like fireworks.
- Visit the National show of the Poultry Club* at Stoneleigh Warks.
- Join a Breed Club.
- Order new equipment and books as Christmas presents.
- Hang greenery in the run in an old string bag so it is easier to peck at.

DIRECTORY

Useful numbers, books to read, places to visit.

Natural Poultry Keeping Dr Batty (Beech Publications)
Onduline roofing for stockists 0207 727 0533
Forsham Cottage Arks housing 01233 820 229
Dixons of Rickinghall dust-free chopped straw 01359 259 341
Cuprinol coloured wood preserver from your DIY store
Sadolin coloured wood preserver from your DIY store

The British Poultry Club Standards (Blackwell Science)
The Orpington Fowl by Will Burdett and Dr. Batty (Beech Publications)
Domestic Fowl Trust catalogue equipment breeds & housing 01386 833 083
Stephen Flory at the Henhouse for breeds and housing 01379 678 644
Mr Potter for breeds 01379 586 288
Hugh Burton breeder Sebrights and others 01954 261 973
Joanna Mayer breeder Sussex and others 01284 787 340
Jonathan Fenning breeder 01473 890 505
Graham Francis transport 01691 860 459
The Poultry Club of Great Britain Secretary 01205 724 081

C & J Wild bird Foods oystershell, corn & sunflower hearts 01743 709 545
Allen and Page Feeds for stockists 01362 822 900
Marriages Feeds for stockists 01245 354 455
Poultry Spice Battle Heywood Bower for stockists 01522 529 206 kg
Eltex feeders and chick drinkers phone for stockists 01384 566 838 kg

Scotland Place Farm for freerange brown eggs 01206 262 293
Martin Pitt for freerange organic eggs 01672 512 035
Munsons for white eggs 01206 272 637
Clarence Court Farm for blue eggs 01384 858 007

Artificial Incubation Dr Batty (Beech Publications)
Keeping a Few hens in your Garden Francine Raymond 01359 268 322 kg

Haxnicks vegetable tunnels for stockists 01747 853 939 kg
Suffolk Herbs for catalogue including green manure seeds 01376 572 456
Seeds of Italy for vegetable, herb & salad seeds 0208 930 2516 kg
Andrew Crace Thai bamboo cloches for stockists 01279 842 685 kg

Intervits soluble vitamins and incubator catalogue 01142 552 340
The Wide Piper rat poison dispenser for stockists 01514 207 151
Diseases of Free Range Poultry by Victoria Roberts (Whittet Books)
Handbook of Herbs by Lesley Bremness (Dorling Kindersley)
The Complete Herbal for Farm and Stable by J de Baïracli Levy (Faber)
Louse Powder from Barrier Biotech for stockists 01953 456 363
Red Mite Powder (organic) from Barrier Biotech 01953 456 363

The Kitchen Garden at Troston near Bury St Edmunds in Suffolk usually
stocks all items marked 'kg' on this list plus lots of other things to please
gardeners, cooks and henlovers. At the time of writing, we are open on
Fridays and Saturdays from Easter till the end of October (closed August).
On Easter Saturday we have a Hen Party with local amateur breeders and an
egg hunt for children. Christmas shopping first weekend in December.
Please phone 01359 268 322 just to make sure.

CRANBERRY AND APPLE CAKE

Eggs are what make cakes light and moist. This one is particularly gooey. Serve warm with vanilla custard - made with your own eggs of course.

For the filling:
2 eating apples, peeled and sliced
3oz/100g caster sugar
8oz/250g cranberries

For the cake:
8oz/250g butter, very soft
8oz/250g caster sugar
Grated zest of a lemon
4 large eggs beaten
8oz/250g plain flour
1 tablespoon baking powder
1 tablespoon lemon juice

Preheat the oven to 375F/190C. Butter and line a 10″/25cm cake tin. For the filling: toss the apple slices with 1 tablespoonful of caster sugar. Put the cranberries, a tablespoon of water and the rest of the 30z/100g sugar in a small saucepan and cook over a gentle heat until the cranberries soften to a jammy consistency. Set aside to cool.

For the cake: put the butter, sugar and lemon zest into a large bowl and beat with a mixer until white and smooth. Add the eggs a little at a time, with a spoonful of flour to avoid curdling. Fold in the sifted flour and baking powder and stir in the lemon juice. Put $^2/_3$ of the cake mixture into the tin, cover with the cranberries and arrange the apple slices on top. Carefully drop the rest of the cake mixture in spoonfuls over the top. Bake for about an hour. Cool in the tin and serve dusted with icing sugar.